Maths BOOSTER

Year 4

Peter Patilla

Letts

EDUCATIONAL

First published 2001

Letts Educational, The Chiswick Centre, 414 Chiswick High Road,
London W4 5TF
Telephone: (020) 8996 3333
Fax: (020) 8742 8390
www.letts-education.com

Text: © Peter Patilla

Author: Peter Patilla

Series project editor: Nancy Terry

Series designer: Ken Vail Graphic Design, Cambridge

Illustrations: Sylvie Poggio Artists Agency (Lisa Williams)

British Library Cataloguing in Publication Data
A CIP record for this book is available from the British Library.

ISBN 1840855886

Printed in the UK

Reprographics by PDQ

Letts Educational, a division of Granada learning Ltd.
Part of the Granada Media Group.

Maths BOOSTER
Year 4

Contents

Place value 4

More or less 5

Rounding 6

Negative numbers 7

Equivalent fractions 8

Fractions of shapes 9

Fractions on number lines 10

Fractions of numbers 11

Fractions and measures 12

Mixed numbers 13

Reading scales 14

Changing units 15

Multiples 16

Square numbers 17

Decimal numbers 1 18

Decimal numbers 2 19

Decimal measures 20

Mental measures 21

Addition 22

Complements 23

Subtraction 24

Brackets 25

Mental calculations 26

Money problems 1 27

Multiplication tables 28

Division facts 29

Functions 30

Calculation words 31

Multiplication TU 1 32

Multiplication TU 2 33

Multiplication 34

Division 1 35

Division 2 36

Remainders 1 37

Remainders 2 38

Money problems 2 39

Measurement problems 40

Time problems 41

Area problems 42

Perimeter problems 43

Polygons 44

Angles 45

Triangles 46

3D shapes 47

Brainbox 48

Place value

What is each number in figures?

1 Three thousand and twenty-six

   a 30 026   b 3026   c 3206

2 Nine thousand and nine

   a 90 009   b 9009   c 9090

3 Sixteen thousand and two

   a 1602   b 16 002   c 160 002

4 Seven thousand six hundred

   a 76 000   b 7060   c 7600

A Which number is halfway between each pair of numbers?

1 (770) (810)

2 (740) (880)

3 (520) (650)

4 (450) (570)

5 (360) (410)

6 (870) (980)

If you are finding numbers that are halfway, work out the difference first. Can you see how this may help?

B Write which number is one more than these.

23 567 These are tens of thousands

1 9099   4 9009   7 29 099

2 9909   5 9990   8 29 999

3 9999   6 29 009   9 29 909

C Look at the number 6387.

Change the order of the figures around to make the biggest even number you can.

More or less

What is 1 more than these numbers?

299	509	759
1 a 310	2 a 510	3 a 750
b 300	b 500	b 705
c 301	c 501	c 760

A

Add on 1 to these.

1 **1099** 3 **3999** 5 **5909**

2 **9999** 4 **9099** 6 **9009**

Add on 10 to these.

7 **7590** 9 **4990** 11 **3090**

8 **9090** 10 **9900** 12 **9990**

Think about the knock-on effect when you add 1 or 10 to some numbers.

B

Subtract 1 from each of these.

1 **3460** 3 **7310** 5 **6290**

2 **1200** 4 **3010** 6 **12 000**

Subtract 10 from each of these.

7 **6500** 9 **4100** 11 **3000**

8 **10 200** 10 **12 000** 12 **10 000**

Subtracting 1 and 10 can be tricky when there are lots of zeros in the number.

C

Copy and fill in the missing numbers.

1 ☐ + 1 = 9999   3 ☐ + 1 = 1111

2 ☐ − 1 = 9999   4 ☐ − 1 = 1111

5

Rounding

Round each number to the nearest 10.

128

1 a 120
  b 130
  c 180

387

3 a 370
  b 380
  c 390

504

5 a 500
  b 510
  c 540

1765

2 a 1760
  b 1770
  c 1750

2084

4 a 2090
  b 2080
  c 2100

5555

6 a 5660
  b 5550
  c 5560

A Round each of these amounts to the nearest 10.

1 £396   6 291 cm   11 599 mℓ

2 £965   7 595 cm   12 992 mℓ

3 £592   8 1993 cm   13 1995 mℓ

4 £1908   9 1096 cm   14 1093 mℓ

5 £3694   10 1996 cm   15 1199 mℓ

> Sometimes when you round to the nearest 10, there is a knock-on into the next hundred.
> **495 rounds up to 500**

B Round each of these amounts to the nearest 100.

1 1975   6 29095   11 £5999

2 2993   7 39910   12 £2095

3 4908   8 59965   13 £7995

4 6950   9 79992   14 £8909

5 7999   10 99499   15 £9999

> Sometimes, when you round to the nearest 100, there is a knock-on into the next thousand.
> **5960 rounds up to 6000**

C What must be added to each number to round it up to the next 1000?

5500   **5015**   **5050**   **5005**

Negative numbers

To which number does each arrow point?

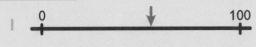

1
```
0          ↓          100
├──────────┼──────────┤
```
a 45   b 55   c 65

3
```
0          ↓          200
├──────────┼──────────┤
```
a 75   b 95   c 105

2
```
0               ↓    500
├────────────────────┤
```
a 205   b 305   c 405

4
```
0          ↓          750
├──────────┼──────────┤
```
a 375   b 275   c 475

A Write the number each arrow points to.

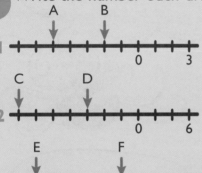

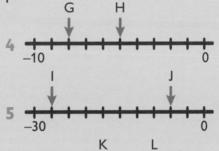

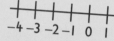

Negative numbers come before zero on a number line. They have a minus sign in front.

```
├──┼──┼──┼──┼──┼──┤
-4 -3 -2 -1  0  1
```

B

1 Which integers lie between 2 and −3?

2 Which odd integers lie between 5 and −5

3 Which even integers lie between −4 and 4?

4 Which integers are more than −2 but less than 3?

5 Which odd integers are less than 5 but more than −2?

Whole numbers are called integers:
4 is a positive integer
−4 is a negative integer
zero is also an integer

C Which temperature does the thermometer show?

```
°C  −10    0    10    20    30    40
```

7

Equivalent fractions

What fraction has been coloured?

1
  a $\dfrac{1}{10}$
  b $\dfrac{1}{7}$
  c $\dfrac{1}{8}$

2
  a $\dfrac{3}{4}$
  b $\dfrac{2}{6}$
  c $\dfrac{6}{10}$

3
  a $\dfrac{1}{7}$
  b $\dfrac{3}{4}$
  c $\dfrac{7}{8}$

A

Copy and write in the missing numbers.

1 $\dfrac{1}{2} = \dfrac{\square}{4}$
  6 $\dfrac{1}{4} = \dfrac{\square}{20}$
  11 $\dfrac{1}{5} = \dfrac{\square}{20}$

2 $\dfrac{1}{2} = \dfrac{\square}{10}$
  7 $\dfrac{1}{3} = \dfrac{\square}{6}$
  12 $\dfrac{1}{5} = \dfrac{\square}{15}$

3 $\dfrac{1}{2} = \dfrac{\square}{8}$
  8 $\dfrac{1}{3} = \dfrac{\square}{9}$
  13 $\dfrac{1}{10} = \dfrac{\square}{20}$

4 $\dfrac{1}{4} = \dfrac{\square}{8}$
  9 $\dfrac{1}{3} = \dfrac{\square}{12}$
  14 $\dfrac{1}{10} = \dfrac{\square}{30}$

5 $\dfrac{1}{4} = \dfrac{\square}{12}$
  10 $\dfrac{1}{5} = \dfrac{\square}{10}$
  15 $\dfrac{1}{10} = \dfrac{\square}{50}$

Equivalent fractions look different but are worth the same. Here are some fractions **equivalent** to a half: $\dfrac{2}{4}$, $\dfrac{3}{6}$, $\dfrac{4}{8}$, $\dfrac{5}{10}$, $\dfrac{50}{100}$

B

Continue each pattern for two more fractions.

1 $\dfrac{1}{2} = \dfrac{2}{4} = \dfrac{3}{6} = \dfrac{4}{8}$
  5 $\dfrac{1}{5} = \dfrac{2}{10} = \dfrac{3}{15} = \dfrac{4}{20}$

2 $\dfrac{1}{3} = \dfrac{2}{6} = \dfrac{3}{9} = \dfrac{4}{12}$
  6 $\dfrac{1}{6} = \dfrac{2}{12} = \dfrac{3}{18} = \dfrac{4}{24}$

3 $\dfrac{1}{4} = \dfrac{2}{8} = \dfrac{3}{12} = \dfrac{4}{16}$
  7 $\dfrac{1}{8} = \dfrac{2}{16} = \dfrac{3}{24} = \dfrac{4}{32}$

4 $\dfrac{1}{10} = \dfrac{2}{20} = \dfrac{3}{30} = \dfrac{4}{40}$
  8 $\dfrac{1}{12} = \dfrac{2}{24} = \dfrac{3}{36} = \dfrac{4}{48}$

Look at the **denominators** of equivalent fractions. Think about **multiples**. Look for a pattern.

C

Which fraction is the odd one out in each set?

A

| $\dfrac{1}{2}$ | $\dfrac{5}{10}$ | $\dfrac{3}{6}$ |
| $\dfrac{8}{14}$ | $\dfrac{6}{12}$ | $\dfrac{10}{20}$ |

B

| $\dfrac{1}{4}$ | $\dfrac{5}{20}$ | $\dfrac{3}{12}$ |
| $\dfrac{4}{16}$ | $\dfrac{4}{12}$ | $\dfrac{10}{40}$ |

Fractions of shapes

Warm up

What fraction has been coloured?

1

  a $\frac{2}{3}$

  b $\frac{3}{4}$

  c $\frac{5}{8}$

2

  a $\frac{3}{8}$

  b $\frac{3}{4}$

  c $\frac{3}{10}$

3

  a $\frac{3}{8}$

  b $1\frac{1}{3}$

  c $1\frac{1}{5}$

A

Write the answers as simple fractions.

1 What fraction is red?

2 What fraction is blue?

3 What fraction is uncoloured?

4 What fraction is coloured?

5 How many more parts must be coloured in to total seven-tenths?

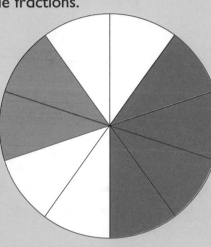

Equivalent fractions are worth the same but look different:

$$\frac{1}{2} = \frac{2}{4}$$

Simple fractions use the smallest numbers:

$\frac{1}{2}$ is simpler than $\frac{2}{4}$

B

Write each fraction as a simple fraction. Put < or > between each pair.

Remember what these signs mean:
< means less than
> means greater than
$\frac{1}{2} < \frac{3}{4}$ $\frac{3}{4} > \frac{1}{2}$

1

3

2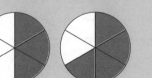

4

C

Copy and write in the missing sign.

$$\frac{2}{3} \;\square\; \frac{4}{6}$$

   $>$

$<$

$=$

9

Fractions on number lines

What fraction is each arrow pointing to?

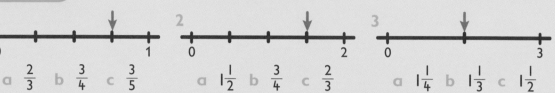

1

a $\frac{2}{3}$ b $\frac{3}{4}$ c $\frac{3}{5}$

2

a $1\frac{1}{2}$ b $\frac{3}{4}$ c $\frac{2}{3}$

3

a $1\frac{1}{4}$ b $1\frac{1}{3}$ c $1\frac{1}{2}$

A

Write the fraction each arrow points to.
Write simple fractions.

Simple fractions use the smallest numbers. $\frac{1}{4}$ is simpler than $\frac{2}{8}$

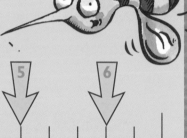

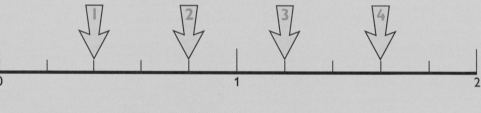

B

Write the fractions the arrows point to.

Check carefully what each mark on the line stands for.

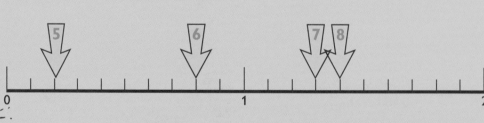

C

Write the fraction being pointed to.

Fractions of numbers

What fraction has been coloured?

1

a $\frac{3}{4}$ b $\frac{1}{2}$ c $\frac{2}{3}$

3
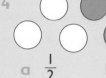

a $\frac{1}{4}$ b $\frac{1}{3}$ c $\frac{1}{6}$

2
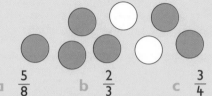

a $\frac{5}{8}$ b $\frac{2}{3}$ c $\frac{3}{4}$

4

a $\frac{1}{2}$ b $\frac{2}{5}$ c $\frac{1}{4}$

A

Copy the tables.
Write the numbers that leave the machine.

In	36	56	76	96	116
Out					

In	10	14	18	22	26
Out					

> To find a quarter, you can halve and then halve again.

B

Find three-quarters of these.

1 £72   3 £104

2 £132   4 £200

> To find $\frac{3}{4}$, work out $\frac{1}{4}$ first.
> To find $\frac{2}{3}$, work out $\frac{1}{3}$ first.

Find two-thirds of these.

5 £69   7 £105

6 £138   8 £201

C

One-fifth of the flour is used.
What weight of flour is left?

Fractions and measures

Warm up

1 What fraction of £1 is 25p?

   a $\frac{1}{2}$ b $\frac{1}{3}$ c $\frac{1}{4}$

2 What fraction of £1 is 10p?

   a $\frac{1}{5}$ b $\frac{1}{10}$ c $\frac{1}{8}$

3 What fraction of £1 is 75p?

   a $\frac{3}{4}$ b $\frac{2}{3}$ c $\frac{7}{10}$

4 What fraction of £1 is 50p?

   a $\frac{1}{4}$ b $\frac{1}{2}$ c $\frac{3}{4}$

A

1 What fraction of 1 kg is 100 g?

2 What fraction of 1 kg is 400 g?

3 What fraction of 1 kg is 600 g?

4 What fraction of 1 kg is 700 g?

5 What fraction of 1 kg is 250 g?

6 What fraction of 1 m is 250 cm?

7 What fraction of 1 m is 750 cm?

8 What fraction of 1 cm is 50 mm?

9 What fraction of $\frac{1}{2}$ m is 25 cm?

10 What fraction of $\frac{1}{2}$ m is 10 cm?

When finding fractions, check that the units are the same.

B

What fraction of the larger bag is the smaller bag?

Check the units are the same and write them as simple fractions.

C

What fraction of a litre is in the container?

Mixed numbers

1 How many halves are there in 3?

  a 3   b 6   c 4

2 How many thirds are there in 2?

  a 6   b 3   c 9

3 How many quarters are there in 4?

  a 4   b 12   c 16

4 How many tenths are there in 1?

  a 9   b 1   c 10

A

Is the numerator greater or less than the denominator?
Copy and write in < or >.

1 $\frac{2}{3}$ numerator ☐ denominator

2 $\frac{4}{3}$ numerator ☐ denominator

3 $\frac{3}{4}$ numerator ☐ denominator

4 $\frac{3}{8}$ numerator ☐ denominator

5 $\frac{7}{5}$ numerator ☐ denominator

6 $\frac{9}{4}$ numerator ☐ denominator

> The top number in a fraction is called the **numerator**.
> The bottom number is the **denominator**.
>
> $\frac{2}{3}$ ← numerator
> ← denominator

> Mixed numbers have whole numbers and fractions.
> $2\frac{2}{3}$

B

Write how many quarters are coloured.
Write each as a mixed number.

1 → $\frac{\square}{4}$ =

2  → $\frac{\square}{4}$ =

3 → $\frac{\square}{4}$ =

4  → $\frac{\square}{4}$ =

C

How many thirds are in each of these mixed numbers?

    $1\frac{1}{3}$ $2\frac{2}{3}$ $3\frac{1}{3}$

Reading scales

Warm up

Which number is each arrow pointing to?

1
0   20
a 4   b 6   c 8

2
0   50
a 20   b 25   c 30

3
0   100
a 50   b 60   c 70

A

How much more liquid is needed to make each container up to 1 litre?

1   2   3   4

1 litre   1 litre   1 litre   1 litre

Check carefully what each mark on the scale stands for.

B

What is the reading on each set of scales?

Read each scale as accurately as you can. Choose whether to write your answers in grams or kilograms.

1   kg   0   1
3   kg   1 2 3 4
5   kg   0   1
7   kg   2   3   4

2   kg   0   1
4   kg   1 2 3 4
6   kg   0   1
8   kg   2   3   4

C

Write the difference in weight between the two readings.

grams   100 200 300 400

grams   100 200 300 400

Changing units

Which measurement is the same?

1 Half a litre.

   a 50 mℓ   b 500 mℓ   c 5000 mℓ

2 Half a centimetre.

   a 5 mm   b 50 mm   c 500 mm

3 Half a kilometre.

   a 50 m   b 500 m   c 5000 m

4 Half a metre.

   a 500 cm   b 50 cm   c 5 cm

A

Write each of these in the smaller unit.

1 $1\frac{3}{4}$ litres = ☐ mℓ

2 $4\frac{1}{4}$ kg = ☐ g

3 $2\frac{1}{2}$ km = ☐ m

4 $3\frac{3}{4}$ m = ☐ cm

Write each of these in the larger unit using fractions.

5 2500 g = ☐ kg

6 3750 m = ☐ km

7 1250 mℓ = ☐ litre

8 825 cm = ☐ m

> You need to know fractions of measurements. Remember what the halves and quarters of large units are.

B

Write each amount in the smaller unit.

1 2.5 m = ☐ cm

2 1.25 ℓ = ☐ mℓ

3 3.5 kg = ☐ g

4 2.75 km = ☐ m

Write each of these in the larger unit using a decimal point.

5 4500 mℓ = ☐ litre

6 575 cm = ☐ m

7 3250 m = ☐ km

8 2250 g = ☐ kg

> Sometimes, a decimal point is used to write mixed units.
> 150 cm = 1.5 m
> 1500 g = 1.5 kg

C

Write these measurements in order.
Start with the smallest.

   2.5 km   2200 m   2.75 km $2\frac{1}{4}$ km   2650 m

Multiples

What is the missing number in each pattern?

1	124	128	☐	136	140

a 130   b 132   c 134

3	66	72	☐	84	90

a 76   b 78   c 80

2	88	96	☐	112	120

a 100   b 102   c 104

4	158	150	☐	134	126

a 142   b 140   c 138

A

1 What is 12th multiple of 4?

2 What is the 13th multiple of 3?

3 What is the 15th multiple of 5?

4 What is the 20th multiple of 2?

5 What is the 50th multiple of 5?

6 What is the 40th multiple of 3?

7 What is the 80th multiple of 5?

8 What is the 100th multiple of 4?

9 What is the 200th multiple of 2?

10 What is the 500th multiple of 10?

Multiples do not stop at the tenth multiple. They on and on and on …

B

Write common multiples of these numbers.

1 (8)   2 (15)   3 (24)   4 (30)   5 (36)

Numbers can be common multiples. 12 is a common multiple of 2, 3, 4 and 6.

Work with common multiples of 3 and 5.

6 What is the smallest common multiple?

7 Which odd common multiples are less than 100?

8 Which even common multiples are less than 100?

C

A digit is missing from each number.
The numbers are multiples of 4.
What could the numbers be?

12☐   1☐2

Square numbers

What is the answer?

1. 3×3
   - a 6
   - b 9
   - c 12

2. 5×5
   - a 10
   - b 20
   - c 25

3. 7×7
   - a 14
   - b 48
   - c 49

4. 9×9
   - a 18
   - b 72
   - c 81

A

Write the square of each of these numbers.

1. 6
2. 8
3. 7
4. 9
5. 4
6. 10
7. 20
8. 30
9. 40
10. 50

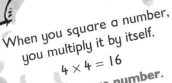

When you square a number, you multiply it by itself.

$4 \times 4 = 16$

16 is a **square number**.

B

What is the result of these?

1. 4^2
2. 9^2
3. 3^2
4. 6^2
5. 2^2
6. 7^2
7. 8^2
8. 5^2
9. 10^2

Here is a short way to write 3×3:

3^2

You say this as 'Three squared'.

$3^2 = 9$

C

Copy the diagram.
Write these numbers on your diagram.

15   16   24   25

	odd number	~~odd number~~
square number		
~~square number~~		

Decimal numbers 1

Match the fraction to its decimal.

1 $\frac{1}{10}$
a 0.1
b 0.01
c 1.0

2 $\frac{3}{10}$
a 3.0
b 0.3
c 0.03

3 $\frac{9}{10}$
a 0.09
b 0.9
c 9.0

4 $\frac{7}{10}$
a 0.7
b 0.07
c 7.0

A Write each decimal as a simple fraction.

1 0.3   4 0.7

2 0.9   5 0.4

3 0.5   6 0.8

0.2 is the same as $\frac{2}{10}$

$\frac{2}{10}$ is equivalent to $\frac{1}{5}$

So 0.2 = $\frac{2}{10}$ = $\frac{1}{5}$

B Write each mixed number as a decimal.

1 $2\frac{1}{10}$ 6 $3\frac{7}{10}$ 11 $5\frac{3}{4}$

2 $5\frac{9}{10}$ 7 $1\frac{1}{2}$ 12 $6\frac{1}{6}$

3 $2\frac{1}{4}$ 8 $4\frac{3}{4}$ 13 $2\frac{1}{10}$

4 $3\frac{1}{5}$ 9 $4\frac{2}{5}$ 14 $7\frac{5}{8}$

5 $6\frac{4}{5}$ 10 $3\frac{1}{4}$ 15 $4\frac{1}{5}$

$2\frac{3}{10}$ is a mixed number.

It is a whole number and a fraction.

It is the same as the decimal 2.3.

C Which decimal number does each arrow point to?

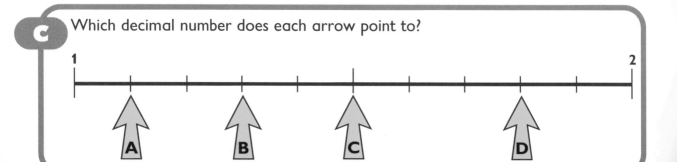

18

Decimal numbers 2

Match the fraction to its decimal.

1 $\frac{40}{100}$

  a 0.04

  b 0.40

  c 4.0

2 $\frac{35}{100}$

  a 3.5

  b 0.35

  c 3.05

3 $\frac{90}{100}$

  a 0.90

  b 0.09

  c 9.0

4 $\frac{25}{100}$

  a 2.5

  b 2.05

  c 0.25

A

Which of these numbers are greater than $2\frac{1}{2}$?

2.25 2.99 2.50 2.15 2.45 2.95 2.75 2.09

Which of these numbers are less than $5\frac{1}{4}$?

5.25 5.50 5.75 5.09 5.90 5.18 5.35 5.20

3.25 as a fraction is $3\frac{25}{100}$

$3\frac{25}{100}$ is equivalent to $3\frac{1}{4}$

B

Copy the number sentences. Write <, > or = in the boxes.

1   4 ☐ 4.00

2   5 ☐ 0.50

3   7 ☐ 70.0

4   3 ☐ 3.000

5   8 ☐ 8.0

6   12.0 ☐ 12.00

7   15.0 ☐ 1.500

8   16.0 ☐ 160.0

9   17.0 ☐ 17.000

10   19.0 ☐ 19.00

11   7.00 ☐ 7.000

12   8.00 ☐ 0.80

13   6.00 ☐ 60.00

14   3.00 ☐ 3.0

15   4.00 ☐ 40.0

Think about whether adding a zero changes a decimal. These are all equivalent:

3
3.0
3.00
3.000

C

Which of these numbers equals 5?

5.00   0.50   0.005   5.0   5.000   0.05

Decimal measures

What is the equivalent measurement?

1 $\frac{1}{2}$ litre

   a 0.5 litre

   b 5.0 litre

   c 0.05 litre

2 $\frac{1}{2}$ kilogram

   a 0.05 kg

   b 0.50 kg

   c 5.00 kg

3 $\frac{1}{2}$ metre

   a 5.0 m

   b 0.05 m

   c 0.50 m

A Record each reading using decimals.

1   2   3

All these measurements are equivalent:

1.2 kg
1.20 kg
1.200 kg
1200 g

B Write each weight in kilograms.

You can write 3560 g as 3.56 kg or 3.560 kg

1   2   3

1750 g   3250 g   3975 g

C How many millilitres are in each bottle?

1·2 L

2·6 L

20

Mental measures

Work these out in your head.

1   1.5 m + 2.5 m   2   3.5 kg + 2.5 kg   3   2.5ℓ + 6.5ℓ   4   3.5 km + 3.5 km

   a   3.0 m   a   6.0 kg   a   8.0ℓ   a   7.0 km

   b   4.0 m   b   5.5 kg   b   8.5ℓ   b   6.0 km

   c   3.5 m   c   6.5 kg   c   9.0ℓ   c   7.5 km

A

Write down the answers.
Try to work them out in your head.

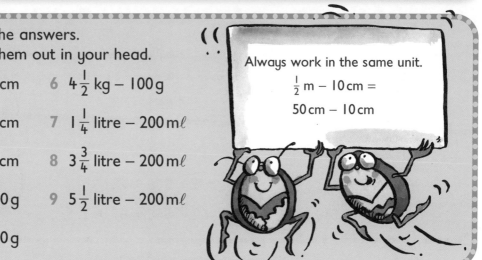

Always work in the same unit.
$$\tfrac{1}{2} \text{ m} - 10 \text{ cm} =$$
$$50 \text{ cm} - 10 \text{ cm}$$

1   $1\frac{1}{2}$ m − 10 cm   6 $4\frac{1}{2}$ kg − 100 g

2   $2\frac{1}{4}$ m − 10 cm   7 $1\frac{1}{4}$ litre − 200 mℓ

3   $3\frac{3}{4}$ m − 10 cm   8 $3\frac{3}{4}$ litre − 200 mℓ

4   $1\frac{1}{4}$ kg − 100 g   9 $5\frac{1}{2}$ litre − 200 mℓ

5   $2\frac{1}{2}$ kg − 100 g

B

Answer these.

1   4 metres − 65 cm   5   5 kg − 150 g   9   2 litres − 300 mℓ

2   10 metres − 5 cm   6   7 kg − 250 g   10   3 litres − 150 mℓ

3   2.5 metres − 35 cm   7   2.5 kg − 50 g   11   1.25 litres − 125 mℓ

4   1.25 metres − 15 cm   8   3.25 kg − 125 g   12   3.75 litres − 250 mℓ

When the units are mixed, choose which one you want to work in.

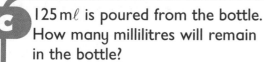

C

125 mℓ is poured from the bottle.
How many millilitres will remain
in the bottle?

2·25 L

21

Addition

Warm up

Work the totals out in your head.

1 128 + 40	3 355 + 30	5 627 + 70
a 528	a 385	a 690
b 168	b 358	b 634
c 132	c 655	c 697
2 286 + 500	4 174 + 700	6 377 + 400
a 786	a 774	a 777
b 768	b 847	b 677
c 886	c 874	c 770

A

Answer these calculations.

1 247 + 75 + 205

2 318 + 465 + 56

3 96 + 175 + 483

4 326 + 64 + 188

5 377 + 65 + 245 + 17

6 138 + 47 + 62 + 394

7 99 + 276 + 751 + 18

8 62 + 508 + 69 + 226

> The order of adding does not matter.
>
> **(126 + 56) + 457**
> is the same as
> **126 + (56 + 457)**

B

The dials show distance travelled in kilometres.

Car A	Car B	Car C
0 1 3 3 7	0 2 8 4 6	0 2 6 7 4

1 What is the total distance travelled by the three cars?

2 Car A travels another 750 km. What will the new reading be?

3 Car B travels another 399 km. What will the new reading be?

4 After a journey car C's reading was 3000 km. How far was the journey?

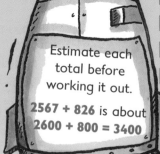

Estimate each total before working it out.

2567 + 826 is about
2600 + 800 = 3400

C

The reading shows how many kilometres a van travelled in May.
In June the van travelled twice as far as it did in May.
What was the reading at the end of June?

0 0 6 5 0

Complements

1 Which pair total 100?

  a 15   75

  b 15   85

  c 15   95

2 Which pair total £1?

  a 35p   75p

  b 35p   55p

  c 35p   65p

3 Which pair total 1 metre?

  a 45 cm   55 cm

  b 45 cm   45 cm

  c 45 cm   65 cm

A

What must be added to these to make £1?

1 17p   2 23p   3 77p   4 93p

What must be added to these to make 1 kg?

5 125 g   6 620 g   7 785 g   8 415 g

What must be added to these to make 1 km?

9 135 m   10 312 m   11 667 m   12 204 m

> 23 and 77 are **complements** of 100 because they total 100.
>
> 350 and 650 are **complements** of 1000 because they total 1000.

B

Write the missing complement to make 1.

1 0.5   5 0.55   9 $\frac{1}{3}$ 13 $\frac{7}{8}$

2 0.1   6 0.85   10 $\frac{2}{5}$ 14 $\frac{3}{10}$

3 0.2   7 0.13   11 $\frac{4}{5}$ 15 $\frac{5}{10}$

4 0.8   8 0.66   12 $\frac{3}{8}$ 16 $\frac{7}{100}$

> 0.3 and 0.7 are **complements** of 1 because they total 1.
>
> $\frac{1}{4}$ and $\frac{3}{4}$ are **complements** of 1 because they total 1.

C

These two angles are complements of 90°.
What is the missing angle?

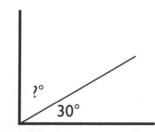

?°

30°

Subtraction

Warm up

Work out the answers in your head.

1. 453 – 112
   - a 441
   - b 341
   - c 351

2. 477 – 225
   - a 352
   - b 225
   - c 252

3. 357 – 224
   - a 133
   - b 123
   - c 135

4. 606 – 302
   - a 403
   - b 304
   - c 326

5. 586 – 324
   - a 262
   - b 242
   - c 226

6. 786 – 362
   - a 424
   - b 462
   - c 526

A

Answer these.

1. 637 – 178
2. 570 – 286
3. 903 – 466
4. 541 – 172
5. 3026 – 174
6. 2196 – 468
7. 1253 – 885
8. 4070 – 804
9. 3072 – 2257
10. 5125 – 1776
11. 8020 – 3343
12. 6123 – 3216

> Estimate each answer before working it out.
>
> 716 – 493 **is about**
> 700 – 500 = 200

B

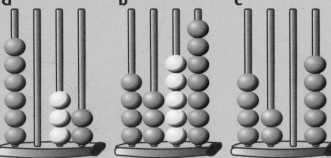

> Try to work answers out in your head before using a pencil and paper method.

1. What is the difference between the smallest and largest numbers?

2. What must you add to **b** to reach 6000?

3. What must you subtract from **a** to equal **b**?

4. What is the smallest difference you can find between the numbers?

C

How many more labels are needed to reach the target?

Collecting Labels		
Month	**Labels collected**	**Target 3000 Labels**
January	367	
February	438	
March	496	

Brackets

Warm up

Work out the answers in your head.

1. 50 − 36
   a 26
   b 24
   c 14

2. 90 − 12
   a 78
   b 82
   c 88

3. 70 − 17
   a 53
   b 67
   c 63

4. 60 − 44
   a 24
   b 26
   c 16

5. 80 − 32
   a 58
   b 52
   c 48

6. 70 − 59
   a 11
   b 29
   c 21

A

Work these out.

1. 20 − (9 + 5)
2. 50 − (8 + 7)
3. 70 − (9 + 9)
4. 80 − (12 − 5)

5. (24 + 26) − 13
6. (80 − 34) + 24
7. (70 − 47) − 19
8. (58 + 62) − 75

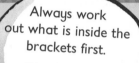

Always work out what is inside the brackets first.
17 − (12 − 9) =
17 − 3 = 14

B

Copy and add brackets to make each answer 50.

1. 72 − 11 + 11
2. 95 − 23 + 22
3. 75 − 12 − 13
4. 17 + 45 − 12

5. 40 − 12 + 22
6. 64 − 30 − 16
7. 42 + 31 − 23
8. 88 − 70 − 32

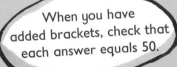

When you have added brackets, check that each answer equals 50.

C

What are the missing numbers?

46 − (◯ − 4) = 22   57 + (◯ − 4) = 90

Mental calculations

Double each number.

1 **26**
   a 42
   b 52
   c 62

3 **47**
   a 94
   b 84
   c 74

5 **79**
   a 148
   b 159
   c 158

2 **38**
   a 66
   b 76
   c 86

4 **56**
   a 106
   b 112
   c 126

6 **95**
   a 180
   b 185
   c 190

A

Work these out in your head.
Knowing doubles might help.
Think carefully about which double to use.

1 58 + 59
2 75 + 78
3 98 + 96
4 84 + 87

5 138 + 139
6 249 + 248
7 427 + 428
8 617 + 619

9 124 + 118
10 139 + 143
11 147 + 154
12 153 + 149

Knowing doubles can help you to work out additions in your head.

double	45 + 45 = 90
near double	45 + 46 = 90 + 1
double	40 + 40 = 80
near double	38 + 36 = 80 − 2 − 4

B

You can use your counting skills to subtract:
* when numbers are close together
   141 − 138
* when one of the numbers is small or a multiple of 10
   127 − 50

Work these out in your head.

1 273 − 268
2 861 − 857
3 1272 − 1266
4 2083 − 2079

5 305 − 8
6 2134 − 7
7 1207 − 8
8 3121 − 13

9 528 − 50
10 1327 − 30
11 3267 − 400
12 2067 − 500

C

The dial shows how far the car has travelled in kilometres.
How many more kilometres must the car travel for the reading to be 24 500 kilometres?

24448

Money problems 1

What is the total?

1 £1.35   75p

    a £2   b £2.10   c £2.20

2 65p   £2.75

    a £3.10   b £3.30   c £3.40

What is the change from £2?

3 68p

    a £1.42   b £1.32   c £1.22

4 £1.15

    a 75p   b 85p   c 95p

A

Here are the prices for a day trip to various towns.

YORK
Adult – £4.99
Child under 14 – £3.50

Skegness
Adult – £7.40
Child under 14 – £4.15

Blackpool
Adult – £10.99
Child under 14 – £5.99

Some problems have several parts. Work out each part carefully.

1 Mr and Mrs Bellamy have three children all under 14 years old. What is the total cost of them all going to York?

2 Mr and Mrs Khan take their children aged 16, 13, 11 and 8 to Blackpool. What will be the total cost?

3 Mrs Martin and her two children aged 15 and 11 pay for the Skegness trip. What will be the change from £20?

B

1 Jack has £6.75 but Jenna has twice as much. How much have they altogether?

2 Hannah buys three items costing £4.24, 89p and £12.99. What will her change be from £20?

3 Asmat bought two books and received £1.45 change from £20. One of the books cost her £14.99. What did the other book cost?

Always check your answers. Read the questions and ask yourself if the result seems sensible.

C

William paid three amounts into his bank. How much did he pay in altogether?

May	£12.36
June	£8.84
July	£24.15

Multiplication tables

Warm up Which multiplication fact matches these answers?

1 56	3 72	5 63
a 6 × 9	a 8 × 9	a 8 × 7
b 7 × 8	b 7 × 8	b 6 × 7
c 9 × 8	c 9 × 7	c 9 × 7
2 54	4 36	6 48
a 4 × 9	a 4 × 9	a 8 × 6
b 9 × 6	b 8 × 4	b 6 × 7
c 7 × 8	c 6 × 7	c 9 × 6

A Answer these.

1 6 × 8 =
   6 × 80 =

4 6 × 7 =
   6 × 700 =

7 7 × 9 =
   70 × 9 =

2 9 × 4 =
   9 × 40 =

5 7 × 5 =
   7 × 500 =

8 8 × 4 =
   80 × 4 =

3 4 × 7 =
   4 × 70 =

6 8 × 8 =
   8 × 800 =

9 6 × 9 =
   60 × 9 =

> You can use facts you know to work out other answers.
> 6 × 9 = 54
> 6 × 90 = 540

B Just write the answers.

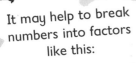

> It may help to break numbers into factors like this:
> 30 × 60 = 3 × 10 × 6 × 10
> = 18 × 100
> = 1800

1 50 × 70	5 40 × 200	9 700 × 50
2 80 × 60	6 60 × 800	10 600 × 90
3 90 × 40	7 70 × 700	11 800 × 40
4 30 × 80	8 90 × 500	12 300 × 70

C Look at the number machine.
Copy and complete the table.

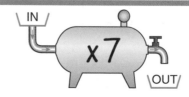

In					
Out	35	56	63	70	700

Division facts

Warm up Answer these.

1 $36 \div 4$
  a 7
  b 8
  c 9

2 $54 \div 6$
  a 9
  b 8
  c 7

3 $56 \div 7$
  a 6
  b 7
  c 8

4 $63 \div 9$
  a 6
  b 7
  c 8

5 $64 \div 8$
  a 9
  b 8
  c 7

6 $72 \div 9$
  a 7
  b 8
  c 9

A Write the missing numbers.

1 $56 \div 7 = \boxed{}$

2 $32 \div 8 = \boxed{}$

3 $48 \div 6 = \boxed{}$

4 $72 \div 9 = \boxed{}$

5 $560 \div 7 = \boxed{}$

6 $320 \div 8 = \boxed{}$

7 $480 \div 6 = \boxed{}$

8 $720 \div 9 = \boxed{}$

9 $5600 \div 7 = \boxed{}$

10 $3200 \div 8 = \boxed{}$

11 $4800 \div 6 = \boxed{}$

12 $7200 \div 9 = \boxed{}$

> Use facts you know to work out other facts.
> $24 \div 3 = 8$
> $240 \div 3 = 80$
> $2400 \div 3 = 800$

B Write the missing numbers.

1 $\boxed{} \div 3 = 13$

2 $\boxed{} \div 5 = 15$

3 $\boxed{} \div 4 = 14$

4 $\boxed{} \div 6 = 17$

5 $\boxed{} \div 6 = 13$

6 $\boxed{} \div 8 = 15$

7 $\boxed{} \div 6 = 14$

8 $\boxed{} \div 9 = 12$

9 $\boxed{} \div 4 = 50$

10 $\boxed{} \div 3 = 80$

11 $\boxed{} \div 6 = 60$

12 $\boxed{} \div 8 = 90$

> Multiplication and division undo each other.
> $72 \div 6 = 12$
> so $12 \times 6 = 72$

C $120 \times 8 = 960$

Copy and put 120, 8 and 960 in the correct boxes.

$\boxed{} \div \boxed{} = \boxed{}$

Functions

What is the answer?

1. (12) double and add 1

   a 23   b 24   c 25

2. (11) add 2 then double

   a 24   b 25   c 26

3. (30) halve then subtract 2

   a 14   b 13   c 12

4. (17) subtract 1 then halve

   a 9   b 7   c 8

A Which number entered each machine?

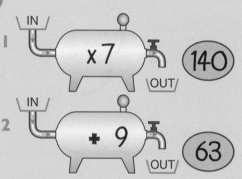

1. IN ×7 OUT (140)

2. IN + 9 OUT (63)

3. IN - 8 OUT (56)

4. IN ÷ 6 OUT (12)

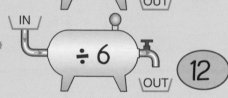

You need to be able to undo some operations.
× undoes ÷   ÷ undoes ×
+ undoes −   − undoes +

B What are the missing numbers?

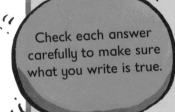

Check each answer carefully to make sure what you write is true.

1. ○ +4 then ×2 20

2. ○ −3 then ÷2 20

3. ○ ×2 then +2 20

4. ○ ÷3 then −3 5

5. ○ ×2 then −21 5

6. ○ ÷5 then +3 5

C Which number entered the machine?

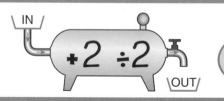

IN +2 ÷2 OUT (10)

Calculation words

Warm up
Answer these.

1 8 plus 3
   a 11
   b 5
   c 24

2 8 minus 3
   a 11
   b 5
   c 24

3 The difference between 8 and 3.
   a 11
   b 5
   c 24

A Write the answers.

1 The product of 17 and 34 is ...

2 58 plus 36 is ...

3 98 halved is ...

4 83 minus 44 is ...

5 56 and 7 have a quotient of ...

6 26 tripled is ...

7 42 and 58 are complements of ...

8 56 increased by 34 is ...

9 72 shared into 3 is ...

10 91 decreased by 46 is ...

Look for the calculation word. Look up the word if you are stuck.

B Answer these word problems.

1 What must be added to 147 to total 250?

2 The sum of two numbers is 576. One number is 277, what is the other?

3 The quotient when dividing by 8 is 30. Which number has been divided?

4 The product of two numbers is 125. One of the numbers is 25, what is the other?

5 The quotient and remainder when dividing by 5 is 7 r4. Which number has been divided?

Read each question carefully. The calculation word does not always tell you what to do.

C Decrease £72 by a third. How much will remain?
Increase £72 by a third. How much will this be altogether?

Multiplication TU 1

What is the answer?

1 40×6
  a 240
  b 204
  c 180

2 20×9
  a 180
  b 160
  c 108

3 50×8
  a 40
  b 400
  c 4000

4 60×6
  a 360
  b 120
  c 180

5 70×7
  a 140
  b 490
  c 409

6 40×8
  a 302
  b 240
  c 320

A

Work out the answers to these.

1 27×6
2 84×7
3 88×5
4 75×5

5 32×9
6 27×8
7 65×7
8 97×4

9 67×5
10 73×9
11 36×8
12 83×8

46×6

Six forties are 240
Six sixes are 36
The answer is 276.

B

Fill in the missing number.

1 $8 \times \triangle = 480$

2 $7 \times \triangle = 490$

3 $6 \times \triangle = 540$

4 $9 \times \triangle = 810$

5 $\triangle \times 70 = 280$

6 $\triangle \times 40 = 360$

7 $\triangle \times 90 = 450$

8 $\triangle \times 70 = 420$

9 $2 \times \triangle = 960$

10 $3 \times \triangle = 960$

11 $4 \times \triangle = 960$

12 $5 \times \triangle = 960$

Look for number patterns and facts you know in these missing number problems.

C

What are the missing digits?

$$\begin{array}{r} 36 \\ \times \bigcirc \\ \hline 2\bigcirc2 \end{array}$$

$$\begin{array}{r} 4\bigcirc \\ \times 8 \\ \hline \bigcirc44 \end{array}$$

Multiplication TU 2

Warm up — What is the answer?

1. 10×16
   - a 160
   - b 1600
   - c 106

2. 10×49
   - a 490
   - b 409
   - c 4900

3. 10×18
   - a 108
   - b 180
   - c 280

4. 10×65
   - a 6500
   - b 605
   - c 650

5. 10×27
   - a 207
   - b 2700
   - c 270

6. 10×80
   - a 800
   - b 8000
   - c 880

A Multiply each number by 9.
Try to answer some in your head.

1. 25   4. 28   7. 67
2. 19   5. 32   8. 83
3. 24   6. 45   9. 99

Here is a quick way to multiply by 9.
$13 \times 9 =$
multiply by 10: $13 \times 10 = 130$
take away the extra number:
$130 - 13 = 117$

B Here is a quick way to multiply by 11.
$13 \times 11 =$
multiply by 10:
$13 \times 10 = 130$
add on the extra number:
$130 + 13 = 143$

Multiply each number by 11.
Try to answer some in your head.

1. 25   4. 28   7. 67
2. 19   5. 32   8. 83
3. 24   6. 45   9. 99

C Which number entered the machine?

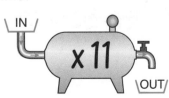

IN → ×11 → OUT 132

Multiplication

What is the answer?

1. 500×6
   - a 3000
   - b 300
   - c 530

2. 300×9
   - a 2700
   - b 270
   - c 1800

3. 300×8
   - a 240
   - b 2400
   - c 1600

4. 700×6
   - a 420
   - b 5600
   - c 4200

5. 700×7
   - a 1400
   - b 4900
   - c 490

6. 400×8
   - a 3200
   - b 320
   - c 2400

A

Work out the answers to these.

1. 120×6
2. 420×5
3. 207×8
4. 412×5
5. 177×8
6. 973×4
7. 360×9
8. 680×7
9. 335×9
10. 623×7
11. 436×5
12. 836×8

324×3

Three three hundreds are 900
Three twenties are 60
Three fours are 12

So the answer is **972**

B

Answer these.

There are lots of different ways to calculate: **36×18**

$36 \times 9 = 324$
$36 \times 18 = 648$

$36 \times 10 = 360$
$36 \times 8 = 288$
$36 \times 18 = 648$

1. 24×16
2. 17×18
3. 32×18
4. 22×15
5. 27×21
6. 32×28
7. 14×12
8. 25×14
9. 36×24
10. 42×14
11. 24×24
12. 45×38

C

What is the missing number?

$$36 \times 24 = 36 \times \boxed{} \times 4$$

Division 1

Warm up

What is the answer?

1. $36 \div 4$
   - a 7
   - b 8
   - c 9

2. $72 \div 8$
   - a 7
   - b 8
   - c 9

3. $42 \div 6$
   - a 6
   - b 7
   - c 8

4. $45 \div 9$
   - a 5
   - b 6
   - c 7

5. $35 \div 7$
   - a 5
   - b 7
   - c 9

6. $56 \div 7$
   - a 7
   - b 8
   - c 9

A

Write the missing numbers.

1. $96 \div 6 = \Box$
2. $88 \div 4 = \Box$
3. $91 \div 7 = \Box$
4. $90 \div 5 = \Box$

5. $\Box \div 5 = 16$
6. $\Box \div 7 = 15$
7. $\Box \div 8 = 19$
8. $\Box \div 6 = 18$

9. $28 \div \Box = 14$
10. $80 \div \Box = 16$
11. $84 \div \Box = 26$
12. $84 \div \Box = 12$

> You can check a division by multiplication.
> $64 \div 4 = 16$
> check: $16 \times 4 = 64$

B

> Look closely at the number being divided. Dividing into multiples of 10 should not be too difficult. Look for table facts to help you.

Try to answer these in your head.

1. $320 \div 8$
2. $630 \div 9$
3. $720 \div 9$
4. $490 \div 7$
5. $540 \div 6$

6. $360 \div 60$
7. $640 \div 80$
8. $300 \div 60$
9. $810 \div 90$
10. $350 \div 70$

11. $500 \div 2$
12. $690 \div 3$
13. $840 \div 6$
14. $960 \div 8$
15. $910 \div 7$

C

Write the missing numbers .

$(25 \div \Box) + 2 = 7$ $(\Box \div 8) - 3 = 6$

Division 2

A

Work out the quotients.

1 2568 ÷ 2   5 2808 ÷ 8   9 4602 ÷ 6

2 1269 ÷ 3   6 3267 ÷ 9   10 2156 ÷ 7

3 5520 ÷ 4   7 3688 ÷ 4   11 1806 ÷ 7

4 7145 ÷ 5   8 5675 ÷ 5   12 8415 ÷ 9

> Estimate what the quotient will be before dividing.
> 1456 ÷ 4
> estimate 1400 ÷ 4
> The quotient will be **between 300 and 400**.

B

Work out the missing numbers.

> The facts are equivalent:
> 156 ÷ ☐ = 26
> 156 ÷ 26 = ☐
> 26 × ☐ = 156
> ☐ ÷ 26 = 156
> This should help you to find the missing numbers.

1 ☐ ÷ 9 = 450   6 ☐ ÷ 4 = 326   11 468 ÷ ☐ = 234

2 ☐ ÷ 4 = 120   7 ☐ ÷ 5 = 774   12 636 ÷ ☐ = 106

3 ☐ ÷ 6 = 370   8 ☐ ÷ 9 = 123   13 868 ÷ ☐ = 217

4 ☐ ÷ 8 = 240   9 ☐ ÷ 7 = 462   14 896 ÷ ☐ = 448

5 ☐ ÷ 5 = 750   10 ☐ ÷ 8 = 337   15 885 ÷ ☐ = 177

C

Now answer this.

37 × 56 = 2072

2072 ÷ 37 =

Remainders 1

What is the remainder?

1 30 ÷ 4
    a 0
    b 1
    c 2

2 67 ÷ 9
    a 4
    b 5
    c 6

3 34 ÷ 6
    a 2
    b 3
    c 4

4 47 ÷ 7
    a 4
    b 5
    c 6

5 39 ÷ 8
    a 6
    b 7
    c 8

6 52 ÷ 6
    a 3
    b 4
    c 5

A

Write the quotient and the remainder.

1 25 ÷ 3

2 57 ÷ 6

3 44 ÷ 7

4 37 ÷ 4

5 47 ÷ 9

6 31 ÷ 7

7 34 ÷ 5

8 29 ÷ 4

9 59 ÷ 6

10 70 ÷ 9

11 23 ÷ 8

12 64 ÷ 7

Think about the largest remainder possible when you divide by 2, 3, 4 and 5, and so on.
Use multiples of the divisor to help you to work out the remainder.

B

Work out each dividend.

1 Divisor 2, quotient 12, remainder 1

2 Divisor 4, quotient 10, remainder 3

3 Divisor 5, quotient 15, remainder 2

4 Divisor 6, quotient 11, remainder 4

5 Divisor 10, quotient 12, remainder 8

6 Divisor 9, quotient 12, remainder 7

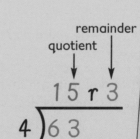

remainder
quotient

$$
\begin{array}{r}
15 \; r\; 3 \\
4\overline{)63}
\end{array}
$$

divisor dividend

Multiplication and division are inverses. They undo each other. Use this fact to check answers.

30 ÷ 7 = 4 r2

Check 4 × 7 = 28, then add the remainder 2 to equal 30.

C

What are the missing divisors?

48 ÷ ☐ = 6 r6   98 ÷ ☐ = 19 r3   70 ÷ ☐ = 23 r1

Remainders 2

Warm up

What is the remainder?

1. 4315 ÷ 10
   - a 15
   - b 5
   - c 315

2. 7562 ÷ 100
   - a 2
   - b 62
   - c 562

3. 5256 ÷ 10
   - a 6
   - b 56
   - c 256

4. 5670 ÷ 100
   - a 7
   - b 70
   - c 67

5. 7349 ÷ 10
   - a 9
   - b 49
   - c 349

6. 7207 ÷ 100
   - a 7
   - b 70
   - c 27

A

Write the answers.

1. Share £1.13 between 3 children. How much will child receive?

2. Share 104 disks amongst 7 children. How many disks will each child have?

3. Share 125 coins into four pots. How many coins are there in each pot?

4. Divide 134 stickers between 5 children. How many will each child get?

5. Arrange 206 marbles into 8 equal sets. How many marbles will there be in each set?

> Sometimes you have to ignore the remainders.

B

Write the answers.

1. Eight children can sit round a table. How many tables will be full if 127 children are seated?

2. Nine people can travel in a minibus. How many minibuses are needed for 111 people?

3. Six stamps are placed on a page. How many pages are filled if I have 200 stamps?

4. Twelve buns fit in each baking tray. How many trays are needed for 125 buns?

5. Pencils are sold in packs of fifteen. How many packs do I need to have 100 pencils?

> Sometimes you have to choose when to round up and when to round down.

C

How many chocolate bars can be bought with £10?

29p

Money problems 2

Divide each amount by 4.

1. **£7**
   - a £1.50
   - b £1.25
   - c £1.75

2. **£13**
   - a £3.25
   - b £3.50
   - c £3.75

3. **£21**
   - a £5.75
   - b £5.25
   - c £5.50

Divide each amount by 5.

4. **£7**
   - a £1.20
   - b £1.40
   - c £1.60

5. **£13**
   - a £2.40
   - b £2.50
   - c £2.60

6. **£21**
   - a £4.50
   - b £4.20
   - c £4.10

A

 25p 17p   33p   57p   46p

Calculate the cost of each box in pounds.

1 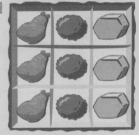 2  3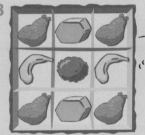

> Some problems have several parts. Work out each part carefully.

B

Find the cost of buying these items.

item	pens	tape	pencils	markers	binders	rulers
unit	5	10	25	6	3	12
price	55p	99p	£1.25	£1.05	£7.15	£1.75

1 25 pens   2 24 markers   3 60 pens   4 30 pencils
5 100 tapes   6 66 markers   7 48 rulers   8 12 binders   9 125 pencils

> Check the **unit price** carefully. The unit price means whether the cost is for 1 or 5 or 10, and so on.

C

Tanya was paid £1.50 for every 50 papers she delivered.
How much was she paid for delivering 250 papers?

Measurement problems

1 How many mℓ in $\frac{1}{4}$ litre?
   a 25
   b 250
   c 2500

2 How many cm in $\frac{1}{4}$ m?
   a 25
   b 250
   c 2500

3 How many g in $\frac{1}{4}$ kg?
   a 25
   b 250
   c 2500

A

1 A teaspoon holds 5 mℓ. How many spoonsful in a quarter litre?

2 How many 25 cm lengths of string can be cut from three-quarters of a metre?

3 How many 50 g weights will balance quarter of a kilogram?

4 A 0.5 litre bottle has 150 mℓ and 250 mℓ poured out. How much remains in the bottle?

5 Five eggs weigh about $\frac{1}{4}$ kg. What will one egg weigh?

6 Two lengths of ribbon are 0.5 m and 1$\frac{1}{2}$ m. What is the difference between them?

You need to know how to write the same measurement in equivalent ways.

500 g = 0.5 kg = $\frac{1}{2}$ kg

B

1 Total 0.5 kg, $\frac{1}{2}$ kg and $\frac{1}{4}$ kg.

2 Total 250 millilitres, $\frac{3}{4}$ litre and $\frac{1}{4}$ litre.

3 Subtract 500 g from 1$\frac{3}{4}$ kg.

4 Subtract 250 mℓ from 0.5ℓ.

5 Total 0.25 m, $\frac{3}{4}$ m and $\frac{1}{2}$ m.

6 Total 0.75 m, $\frac{1}{2}$ m and $\frac{1}{4}$ m.

7 Subtract 750 mℓ from 1$\frac{1}{4}$ ℓ.

8 Subtract 150 g from 0.25 kg.

Look at the units very carefully.
You might need to change:
metres to cm
kilograms to g
litres to mℓ

C

A large apple weighs about 250 g.
How many large apples will weigh 2$\frac{1}{2}$ kg?

What will 20 large apples weigh?

Time problems

What is the answer?

1. How many minutes are there in $\frac{1}{4}$ hour?

   a 25
   b 15
   c 30

2. How many seconds are there in $\frac{1}{4}$ minute?

   a 25
   b 15
   c 45

3. How many hours are there in $\frac{1}{2}$ day?

   a 12
   b 24
   c 30

A

The clock shows the time for the evening meal.

1. The pie takes 45 minutes to cook. When must it go in the oven?

2. The vegetables take 25 minutes to prepare and cook. When must they be started?

3. A pudding takes 1 hour and 40 minutes to cook. It was started at 5:50. Will it be ready in time?

> When calculating with time, remember that there are 60 minutes in one hour.

B

1. How many buses reach Denton before noon?

2. How long is the quickest journey between Amley and Denton?

3. Which bus from Barnster reaches Copthorne at quarter past twelve?

4. How long does it take the 11:50 bus from Barnster to reach Denton?

Amley	10:15	10:35	11:00	11:20	11:55
Barnster	10:35	10:55	11:20	11:50	12:15
Copthorne	10:50	11:05	11:35	12:05	12:30
Denton	11:05	11:20	11:50	12:20	12:45

> The first two numbers tell the hour and the next two the minutes past the hour. 11:35 is 35 minutes past 11 o'clock.

C

A computer game lasted 2 minutes and 25 seconds. How many seconds did it last?

Area problems

What is the answer?

1 7×8
 a 72
 b 64
 c 56

2 8×8
 a 16
 b 64
 c 56

3 9×6
 a 54
 b 56
 c 63

4 7×7
 a 48
 b 14
 c 49

5 6×8
 a 48
 b 54
 c 56

6 9×9
 a 18
 b 81
 c 72

A How many square cm does each shape cover?

1
4 cm

4 cm

2
3 cm

5 cm

3
4 cm

6 cm

Area is how much surface a shape has.

4 cm

3 cm

The area of this rectangle is 3×4 square centimetres.

B

A short way of writing square centimetres is **cm²**

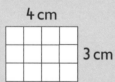

4 cm

3 cm

The area of this rectangle is 12 cm².

Write the area of each shape in cm².

5 cm

3 cm

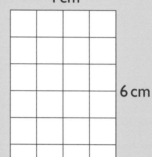
5 cm

5 cm

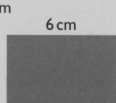
6 cm

5 cm

C The area of a square is 9 cm².
How long is each side?

Perimeter problems

What is the answer?

1 **12 + 12 + 15 + 15**
    a 42
    b 52
    c 54

3 **17 + 15 + 17 + 15**
    a 62
    b 64
    c 54

5 **13 + 18 + 18 + 13**
    a 56
    b 52
    c 62

2 **15 + 15 + 15 + 15**
    a 60
    b 50
    c 55

4 **12 + 12 + 12 + 12**
    a 36
    b 48
    c 46

6 **19 + 19 + 19 + 19**
    a 78
    b 76
    c 74

A What is the perimeter of each regular shape in centimetres?
Each side measures 7 cm.

Perimeter is the distance all the way round a shape.

B What is the perimeter of each shape in centimetres?

1
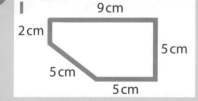
9 cm, 2 cm, 5 cm, 5 cm, 5 cm

2
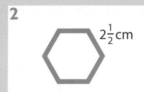
$2\frac{1}{2}$ cm

3
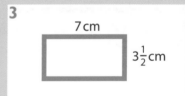
7 cm, $3\frac{1}{2}$ cm

You will need to work out any missing lengths before finding each perimeter.

4
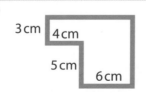
3 cm, 4 cm, 5 cm, 6 cm

5
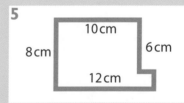
10 cm, 8 cm, 6 cm, 12 cm

C The perimeter of this square is 96 cm.
How long is each side?

Polygons

What are the names of these shapes?

1

a pentagon
b octagon
c hexagon

2

a pentagon
b octagon
c hexagon

3

a pentagon
b octagon
c hexagon

A Complete each word.
Use 'concave' or 'convex'.
Use -agon words such as 'pentagon' and 'hexagon'.

Concave polygons

Convex polygons

1 con ___ ___agon

2 con ___ ___agon

3 con ___ ___agon

4 con ___ ___agon

5 con ___ ___agon

6 con ___ ___agon

B Write whether each polygon is 'regular' or 'irregular'.
Complete the -agon words.

Regular polygons have all their sides the same length. all angles are also the same size.

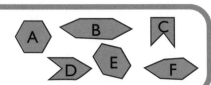

regular   irregular

1 _____ ___agon

2 _____ ___agon

3 _____ ___agon

4 _____ ___agon

5 _____ ___agon

6 _____ ___agon

C Which polygon is the odd polygon out in this set?
Complete the sentence.

Polygon [ ] is the odd one out because _____

A   B   C
D   E   F

Angles

Warm up

What are the sizes of these angles?

1
   a 45°
   b 60°
   c 90°

2
   a 45°
   b 60°
   c 90°

3
   a 45°
   b 60°
   c 90°

A

Write whether each angle is 'acute', 'right angled' or 'obtuse'.

Acute angles are between 0° and 90°.
Right angels are exactly 90°.
Obtuse angles are between 90° and 180°.

acute angle   right angle   obtuse angle

1
4
2
5
3
6

B

Each angle is one of these 30°, 45°, 60° or 90°.
Write the size of each angle.

Right angle = 90°   Half right angle = 45°

One-third right angle = 30°   Two-thirds right angle = 60°

1
4
2
5
3
6

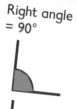

C

Write the order of these angles.
Start with the smallest.
Record whether each angle is
'acute', 'obtuse' or 'right-angled'.

 A
B
C
 D
 E
 F

Triangles

What are the names of these quadrilaterals?

1
a square
b rectangle
c kite

2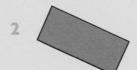
a square
b rectangle
c kite

3
a square
b rectangle
c kite

A Write the name of each type of triangle.
Use the words 'equilateral', 'isosceles' or 'scalene'.

1

2

3

4

5

6

You can describe triangles by their sides.
Three sides the same = **equilateral**
Two sides the same = **isosceles**
No sides the same = **scalene**

equilateral   isosceles   scalene

B Write the name of each type of triangle.
Use the words 'right angled', 'acute' or 'obtuse'.

1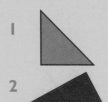

2

3

4

5

6

You can describe triangles by angles.
One right angle = **right-angled triangle**
All acute angles = **acute-angled triangle**
One obtuse angle = **obtuse-angled triangle**

right angled
one angle 90°

acute
all angles less
than 90°

obtuse
one angle more
than 90°

C Which triangle is the odd one out in this set?
Complete the sentence.

Triangle ☐ is the odd one out because _____

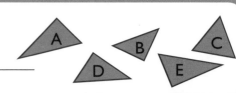

3D shapes

1

   a pyramid
   b prism
   c cone

2

   a cone
   b hemisphere
   c sphere

3

   a prism
   b pyramid
   c cuboid

A Name each of these polyhedra.

1 The polyhedron with 6 square faces is …

2 The polyhedron with 2 triangle and 3 rectangle faces is …

3 The polyhedron with 2 square and 4 rectangle faces is …

4 The polyhedron with 4 triangle faces is …

5 The polyhedron with 1 square face and 4 triangle faces is …

6 The polyhedron with 6 rectangle faces is …

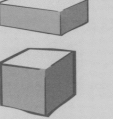

> Any 3D shape that has all flat faces is called a **polyhedron**.
>
> Several polyhedron are called **polyhedra**.
>
> Cubes, cuboids, pyramids and prisms are all different kinds of polyhedra.

> Shapes that have curved faces are not called polyhedra.

B These are half of 3D shapes.
Name each whole shape and say which are polyhedra.

C Write the names of the 3D shapes that will pass through the hole.

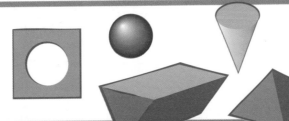
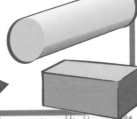

47

Brainbox

Write the answers to these problems.

Try to answer each one in your head.

Some questions are quite hard.

1 How many millimetres are in $1\frac{1}{2}$ centimetres?

2 Which number is 99 more than 4070?

3 What must be added to 520 mℓ to make $\frac{3}{4}$ litre?

4 What is the difference between £4.96 and £5.07?

5 What is the twelfth multiple of 15?

6 What is $\frac{3}{4}$ of £10?

7 What is the missing number?

$23 = (5 \times \boxed{}) - 7$

8 What must you add to 3675 to round it up to the next 100?

9 How many minutes between 7:45 and 8:05?

10 Which number divided by 2 equals 37?

11 How many 15 mℓ spoonsful are in a 300 mℓ bottle?

12 What is 26×6?

13 What is half of 130?

14 What is the missing number?

$18 \times \boxed{} = 54$

15 What is $383 - 78$?

16 Subtract 999 from 7350

17 What is $840 \div 4$?

18 What is remainder when you divide 5671 by 100?

19 What is a third of £2.70?

20 What is the missing number?

$\boxed{} + 39 = 184.$

More than 15 is fantastic!

How did you do?

Well done if you scored more than 10.